DIABE

Type 2

HEALING
C◯DE

Ingredients. Ultimate Weight Loss Cookbook

What I can eat to prevent and reverse diabetes.

DIABETES TYPE 2 HEALING CODE
5 INGREDIENTS. ULTIMATE WEIGHT LOSS COOKBOOK

ISBN: 9781913005467

DISCLAIMER

CONTENTS

SIDES

DESSERTS AND SWEET TREATS

INTRODUCTION

If you or a loved one has recently been diagnosed with prediabetes or type 2 diabetes, then you'll know it can be a frightening, stressful, and confusing time.

There is no getting around the fact that diabetes is a serious condition. However, the good news is you can manage, and potentially reverse your diabetes by following a specially designed diet.

Whilst diabetes remains an incurable disease, it can be reversed. On a regular basis, GPs and health practitioners are giving patients the incredible news that their diabetes has gone into remission; which basically means glucose levels have returned to normal without the need for medications to control them.

So, what's changed with our understanding and treatment of diabetes over recent years? It's long been known that if you eat sweet, sugary foods and are obese you have a greater likelihood of developing diabetes - perhaps even as early as in your twenties or thirties.

Keeping your weight in check therefore helps reduce your chances of developing type 2 diabetes and a low calorie, low carb, low GI diet, may even be able to REVERSE diabetes.

DIRECT

Scientists leading the DiRECT (short for Diabetes Remission Clinical Trial), Professors Mike Lean and Roy Taylor, have recently detailed excellent results.

The Lancet published report shows just how effective a weight loss approach to type 2 diabetes can be. In fact, after 12 months almost half of the 300 participants were in remission from their diabetes.

Furthermore, the Newcastle and Glasgow University study found the greater the weight loss, the higher the chance of remission. 86% of those who lost more than 15kg saw their diabetes go into remission. There were still highly effective remission rates in those that lost between 10 and 15kg (57%); and remission was achieved for 34% of those losing 5 to 10kg, or just 1 to 2 stone.
This was compared with standard diabetes care, where patients rarely saw their diabetes go into remission, with a rate of just 4% after 12 months.
As a result of this and other research, the NHS is now rolling out new programmes. These nationwide programmes will not only improve the lives of thousands of patients, but they will make up part of further research to better our understanding of the condition. Speak to your GP about how you can prevent, manage and even reverse diabetes.

You should be aware that following a low-calorie diet can increase the likelihood of hypos. It is therefore imperative you speak to your GP before starting any diet. They may be able to change your medication and keep a close eye on your blood sugar levels.

THE BASICS

The main aspect of diabetics is the body's inability to control blood sugar, which can be affected by carbohydrates. You, therefore, need to carefully control carbohydrates yourself. You may also be advised to eat a snack every 2-3 hours to maintain your blood sugar levels.

While it varies from person to person, you may be advised to keep your meals to between 45 and 60 grams of carbohydrates, and a snack between 15 and 30 grams of carbohydrate. Most common foods contain some carbohydrate so it's important to learn about different foods:

- No Carb - meat, fish, and eggs are carb-free. Can be eaten freely.
- Low Carb - cheese, milk, and yoghurt contain small amounts of carbohydrate, as do beans, legumes, and many vegetables and fruits. Make up a large part of a diabetic-friendly diet.
- Med/High Carb - starchy vegetables such as potatoes and corn as well as grains including rice, pasta, and bread are carbohydrate-rich foods. Should be swapped for diabetic friendly options and controlled.
- High Carb - all sweet foods such as chocolate, desserts, cakes, and sugary drinks have very high carbohydrate contents. To be avoided and eaten only in small amounts. Swap for diabetic-friendly options.

GI FOODS

If it were just about counting carbs, then life would be so much easier for people with diabetes. However, as you know, there is the glycaemic count to consider.

The glycaemic index shows how rapidly the blood sugar is affected when a food is eaten. As a diabetic, it's recommended to avoid foods with a GI higher than 55 which can cause a spike in blood sugar. The main changes you will need to make are to find low GI food alternatives to staples and favourites. This means changing from staples such as white bread, rice, pastas and potatoes to foods from which carbohydrates are released more slowly. These include foods such as whole wheat pasta, konjac noodles, brown rice, sweet potatoes, and rye bread.

To further confuse matters, you can actually change the GI of a food. Remember - this is a scale of how easily the carbohydrates is released. So, for example, if you grind food and make it more easily digested, the higher you will increase the glycaemic count. Whole wheat kernels have a lower GI than milled wholewheat, for example. Similarly, al dente pasta has a lower GI than pasta cooked for longer, which is more easily digested.

TOP SUPER HEALING FOODS FOR DIABETICS

You'll find the recipes in this book use carefully chosen with ingredients that are high fibre and low fat; they're also low GI and low calorie. In addition, we have included plenty of superfood ingredients, which have been carefully chosen for their healing properties in terms of diabetes:

- Nuts
- Eggs
- Greek Yoghurt
- Strawberries
- Shirataki or Konjac Noodles
- Squash
- Leafy Greens
- Broccoli

- Olive Oil
- Flax Seeds
- Chia Seeds
- Fatty Fish
- Turmeric
- Cinnamon
- Garlic
- Apple Cider Vinegar

A NOTE ABOUT EXERCISE

It's best to follow this diet with regular exercise, which has several benefits including improved mental health, stronger bones and reduced risk of cardiac disease. Build up to a regular exercise plan so your energy intake will be increased and your weight loss more rapid. The sooner you lose weight, the faster your diabetes could go into remission.

Aim for at least moderate exercise while you follow this plan. The long-term recommended goal for health is to exercise five days a week, for at least 30 minutes.

JUST 5 INGREDIENTS?

We think life's hard enough, especially when you are coming to terms with a diabetes diagnosis, so we've tried to make things easy with just 5 ingredients in all our recipes. To make the recipes in this book, keep your store cupboard stocked with these diabetic-friendly ingredients:

- Olive oil, vegetable oil, and cooking spray
- Salt and pepper
- Herbs including thyme, rosemary, bay leaves, basil, and oregano.
- Spices including cinnamon, curry, chilli, and ginger.
- Garlic cloves
- Tinned tomatoes
- Tomato pasta sauce
- Balsamic vinegar, red wine vinegar, white wine vinegar, and apple cider vinegar
- Worcester sauce
- Tomato ketchup
- Gravy powder

- Whole grain mustard
- Whole wheat pasta
- Red lentils
- Low-fat coconut milk
- Stock cubes
- Stevia
- Vanilla extract
- Baking powder
- Flour including plain, self-raising, wholemeal, almond, coconut, and cornflour.
- Soy sauce
- Cocktail sticks and paper bun cases

All the recipes in this book are calorie-controlled - but that doesn't mean they are bland. For example, you could have Healthy Low-Carb Coconut Flour Pancakes or Quinoa Hazelnut Porridge for breakfast. Lunch dishes are around 300 calories; choose from dishes such as Crustless Cheddar & Broccoli Quiche (page 31) and Cheesy Tomato Pasta Bake (page 16). For dinner, we have put together a selection of mouth-watering dishes, all with a calorie count below 500, including Beef & Vegetable Pie (page 44), Herb Crusted Lamb (page 51), and Salmon and Prawn Fusilli (page 56).

Obviously, desserts full of sugar are very dangerous for people with diabetes. However, we have used some clever tricks to make some diabetic desserts and cakes that will satisfy any sweet cravings. Desserts include Healthy Chocolate Ice Cream (page 91) and High Protein Berry Crumble (page 79) with Rich Custard (page 92). We have also used ingredients such as Stevia and almond flour to make delicious cakes including Grandma Sue's Sugar-free Chocolate Cake (page 84) and Pumpkin Raspberry Muffins (page 80).

A calorie total for the day of around 1200 - 1500 is suitable for weight loss but it's important that you speak to your GP before you commence this diet. Monitor your progress in terms of pounds lost, but also other health indicators including your blood sugar.

Keep focused on your goal of reversing diabetes and you'll be motivated to stay on track.

Best of luck!

DIABETES *Type 2* HEALING C⟳DE

LUNCHES & SNACKS

SLOW COOKER CHICKEN WITH SWEET POTATOES

Nutrition Facts
Per Serving
Calories 257
Total Carbs 27g
Net Carbs 22g

5 Ingredients

- 4 125g/4oz boneless, skinless chicken thighs
- 1 onion, chopped
- 450g/1lb sweet potatoes, peeled and sliced
- 750ml/1¼pts chicken stock
- 2 tbsp Dijon mustard

Method

1 Place the chicken in a slow cooker or you can use a large pan with a tight-fitting lid.

2 Now add the onions and sweet potatoes.

3 Add the remaining ingredients and cook on low for 5-7 hours in your slow cooker. If you're using the stovetop method, bring to the boil and reduce to a low simmer, then cook for around 3 hours.

4 Remove the bay leaf and serve.

FROM YOUR STORE CUPBOARD
1 tbsp Stevia
¼ tsp thyme
1 bay leaf

VEGETABLE NOODLE STIR-FRY

Nutrition Facts
Per Serving
Calories 169
Total Carbs 31g
Net Carbs 25g

5 Ingredients

- 450g/1lb sweet potato
- 225g/8oz carrots
- 225g/8oz courgettes/zucchini

- 1 shallot, diced
- 1 red chilli, diced

Method

1 Peel and spiralize the sweet potato, courgettes, and carrots by using a mandolin, grater or a vegetable peeler to create long, thin noodles.

2 Use a vegetable stock cube and boiling water to make a small amount of vegetable stock.

3 Heat a large wok until very hot and add 2 tablespoons of the vegetable stock.

4 When the stock boils add all the ingredients except the courgette and stir fry for 2 minutes.

5 Now add the courgettes, and cook for a further 2 minutes.

6 Season with salt and pepper, and serve in a large bowl, drizzled with the olive oil.

FROM YOUR STORE CUPBOARD

¼ vegetable stock cube
1 tbsp olive oil
2 garlic cloves, crushed
Salt and pepper

QUICK BROWN RICE STIR FRY

Nutrition Facts
Per Serving
Calories 267
Total Carbs 37g
Net Carbs 34g

5 Ingredients

- 25g/1oz spring onions, sliced
- 75g/3oz lean ham, cubed
- 150g/5oz frozen peas and carrots, thawed
- 200g/7oz cooked brown rice
- 1 egg, beaten

Method

1 Heat the oil in a wok and fry the spring onions and ham for 2 minutes over a medium high heat.

2 Add the remaining ingredients except for the egg and cook for a further 3 minutes.

3 Push the mixture to one side then add the egg to the wok.

4 Leave for 1-2 minutes until the egg is set, then mix the egg through the rice.

5 Serve immediately.

FROM YOUR STORE CUPBOARD
2 tsp vegetable oil
1 tsp light soy sauce
Pepper

LOW-CALORIE POTATO AND PEA CURRY

SERVES 4

Nutrition Facts
Per Serving
Calories 289
Total Carbs 45g
Net Carbs 35g

5 Ingredients

- 2 medium onions
- 3 medium potatoes, peeled and diced
- 400g/14oz frozen cauliflower

- 200g/7oz frozen peas
- 200g/7oz cooked brown rice

Method

1 Heat the oil in a large heavy-based saucepan and fry the onions for 5 minutes until soft.

2 Add the curry powder and cook for 1 minute.

3 Stir in the potato and coat well.

4 Now add the tomatoes and stock prepared with the stock cube and boiling water.

5 Bring to the boil, cover the pan with a lid and cook for 20 minutes or until the potatoes are tender.

6 Stir in the coconut milk and cauliflower and cook for a further 10 minutes.

7 Add the peas for the final 5 minutes.

8 Serve with the cooked brown rice.

FROM YOUR STORE CUPBOARD

2 tsp curry powder
200ml/7floz low-fat coconut milk
300g/10½oz diced canned tomatoes
¼ vegetable stock cube
100ml/3½floz boiling water
1 tsp vegetable oil

15

CHEESY TOMATO PASTA BAKE

Nutrition Facts
Per Serving
Calories 302
Total Carbs 36g
Net Carbs 27g

5 Ingredients

- 100g/3½oz mushrooms
- 125g/4oz sweetcorn
- 4 tbsp fresh basil
- 75g/3oz low-fat ricotta cheese
- 125g/4oz mozzarella cheese, chopped

Method

1 Heat the oil in a large pan and fry the mushrooms for a few minutes until soft.

2 Add the tomato pasta sauce and bring to the boil.

3 Remove from the heat and stir in the sweetcorn, pasta, ricotta cheese, and basil.

4 Divide the pasta mixture into 4 individual gratin dishes.

5 Top with the mozzarella and place under a hot grill until bubbling and golden

FROM YOUR STORE CUPBOARD
200g/7oz whole wheat penne, cooked to al dente and drained
1 tbsp olive oil
320ml/12½oz tomato pasta sauce

FAST CREAMY CURRIED BUTTERNUT SOUP

Nutrition Facts
Per Serving
Calories 174
Total Carbs 33g
Net Carbs 28g

5 Ingredients

- 1 butternut squash, halved and roasted
- 120ml/4floz reduced-fat crème fraîche/sour cream
- ¼ tsp lime zest
- 1 tbsp lime juice
- 3-4 ice cubes

Method

1 Use a large spoon to scoop the flesh from the roasted butternut squash and place in a large saucepan.

2 Prepare the stock by combining the stock cube with the boiling water and add to the pan.

3 Add the garlic, onion, and curry powder, as well as salt and pepper to the pan.

4 Bring to the boil and simmer for 10 minutes.

5 Place the soup in a blender and puree until smooth.

6 In a small bowl, mix together the crème fraiche with the lime zest and juice.

7 Serve the soup with a generous spoonful of lime crème fraiche.

FROM YOUR STORE CUPBOARD

1¼ vegetable stock cubes
600ml/1pt boiling water
1 tsp garlic powder
1 tsp onion powder
1 tsp curry powder
Salt and pepper

CREAMY MUSHROOM SOUP

Nutrition Facts
Per Serving
Calories 221
Total Carbs 13g
Net Carbs 10g

5 Ingredients

- 450g/1lb mushrooms, sliced
- 1 large onion, diced

- 1 400g/14oz can of coconut milk

Method

1 Fry the onion, garlic, and mushrooms in a large heavy-based pan over a medium heat for approximately 10 minutes.

2 Make ¾ pint of stock, using 1 vegetable stock cube and boiling water.

3 Add the stock and remaining ingredients to the pan and bring to the boil.

4 Simmer the soup for around 15 minutes on a low heat.

5 Blend the soup in a food processor and serve garnished with thyme if desired.

FROM YOUR STORE CUPBOARD
1 tsp olive oil
1 vegetable stock cube
1 tbsp soy sauce
1 garlic clove, crushed
Salt and pepper to taste

CELERY, SWEET POTATO, AND BEAN SOUP

Nutrition Facts
Per Serving
Calories 250
Total Carbs 39g
Net Carbs 26g

5 Ingredients

- 5 stalks of celery, chopped into small pieces
- 250g/9oz sweet potato, chopped into small pieces
- 400g/14oz canned butter beans
- 4 tbsp fresh parsley
- 3-4 ice cubes

Method

1 Heat the oil in a non-stick saucepan and sauté the celery for 4 minutes.

2 Add the sweet potato and pour in water to cover the vegetables by around 3cm/1-inch.

3 Season, bring to the boil and reduce to a simmer.

4 After 20 minutes add the butter beans and continue to cook for a further 5 minutes.

5 Blend the soup to a puree; you can add extra water if the soup is thicker than you'd like.

6 Stir in the garlic and parsley and serve immediately.

FROM YOUR STORE CUPBOARD

1 tbsp olive oil
1 garlic clove
Salt and pepper

CREAMY RED LENTIL SOUP

Nutrition Facts
Per Serving
Calories 220
Total Carbs 33g
Net Carbs 27g

5 Ingredients

- 100g/3½oz red lentils
- 1 small onion, chopped
- 1 carrot, chopped
- 2 tbsp reduced-fat crème fraiche/sour cream
- 1 tbsp fresh parsley, chopped

Method

1 Make the stock by blending the stock cube with the boiling water.

2 In a large pan, combine the stock, lentils, onion, garlic, and carrot.

3 Bring to the boil and simmer for 25 minutes or until the lentils are tender.

4 Blend the soup in a food processor and season to taste.

5 Serve topped with crème fraîche and parsley.

FROM YOUR STORE CUPBOARD
1 garlic clove, crushed
1¼ vegetable stock cubes
600ml/1pt boiling water
Salt and pepper

CREAM OF ASPARAGUS SOUP

Nutrition Facts
Per Serving
Calories 151
Total Carbs 14g
Net Carbs 11g

5 Ingredients

- 15g/½oz reduced-fat margarine
- 1 small onion, finely chopped
- 125g/4oz asparagus, chopped
- 150ml/5floz full-fat milk
- 3-4 ice cubes

Method

1 Melt the margarine in a large heavy-based pan and fry the onion and asparagus for 3 minutes.

2 Add the flour and cook for 1 minute.

3 Make the stock by blending the stock cube with the boiling water.

4 Add the stock slowly to the pan, stirring to incorporate the flour without lumps.

5 Bring to the boil and reduce to a simmer for 10 minutes or until the asparagus is tender and cooked.

6 Add the milk then blend until smooth in a food processor.

7 Season with salt and pepper and serve.

FROM YOUR STORE CUPBOARD

25g/1oz plain flour
1 vegetable stock cube
450ml/15½floz boiling water
Salt and pepper

MULLIGATAWNY SOUP

Nutrition Facts
Per Serving
Calories 123
Total Carbs 23g
Net Carbs 20g

5 Ingredients

- 1 small onion, finely chopped
- 1 small carrot, diced
- 1 140g/5oz sweet potato, diced
- 1 tbsp medium curry paste
- 40g/1½oz basmati rice

Method

1 Heat the oil in a large pan and fry the onion gently for 5 minutes until soft.

2 Add the carrot and sweet potato and fry for a further 5 minutes.

3 Add all the remaining ingredients except the rice and bring to the boil.

4 Cover the pan and simmer for 15 minutes.

5 Cook the rice in a large pan of boiling water. Drain the rice and set aside.

6 Blend the soup in a food processor until smooth.

7 To serve, stir in the rice. Garnish with fresh coriander/cilantro if desired.

FROM YOUR STORE CUPBOARD

1 tsp vegetable oil
1 200g/7oz tin tomatoes
40g/1½oz red lentils
1 garlic clove, crushed
1 vegetable stock cube
1litre/1½pts boiling water

PARSNIP AND APPLE SOUP

Nutrition Facts
Per Serving
Calories 160
Total Carbs 26g
Net Carbs 16g

5 Ingredients

- 1 small onion, chopped
- ½ tsp cumin seeds
- 300g/11oz parsnips, peeled
- 1 small cooking apple, peeled and chopped
- 3-4 ice cubes

Method

1 Heat the oil in a large pan and fry the cumin seeds and onions for 3 minutes.

2 Add the apple and parsnips and fry for a further 3 minutes.

3 Make the stock by blending the stock cube with the boiling water, and add to the pan.

4 Bring to the boil and simmer for 25 minutes or until the parsnips are cooked through and tender.

5 Puree the soup in a food processor.

6 Season to taste and serve.

FROM YOUR STORE CUPBOARD
600ml/1pt boiling water
1¼ vegetable stock cubes
1 tsp vegetable oil
Salt and pepper

VEGETABLE FRITTATA

Nutrition Facts
Per Serving
Calories 130
Total Carbs 7g
Net Carbs 6g

5 Ingredients

- 125g/4oz broccoli, chopped into small pieces
- 125g/4oz baby plum tomatoes, cubed
- 25g/1oz spinach, washed and finely chopped
- 4 eggs
- 120ml/4floz skimmed milk

Method

1 Preheat the oven to 350F/180C/Gas Mark 4.

2 Mix the vegetables, garlic powder, oregano, salt, and pepper together in a bowl.

3 Heat the oil in a non-stick frying pan that can be used in the oven.

4 Fry the vegetables for 2 minutes.

5 In a small bowl, beat the eggs together with the milk.

6 Pour the egg mixture into the pan and make sure the vegetables and eggs are evenly spread out.

7 Bake the frittata in the oven for 10 minutes.

8 Use a skewer to ensure the frittata is cooked through.

9 Slice into 4 wedges and serve with a green salad.

FROM YOUR STORE CUPBOARD

1 tbsp olive oil
1 tsp garlic powder
1 tsp dried oregano
Salt and pepper

OATMEAL BREAKFAST SMOOTHIE

Nutrition Facts
Per Serving
Calories 368
Total Carbs 42g
Net Carbs 35g

5 Ingredients

- 50g/2oz uncooked oats
- 2 frozen bananas
- 750ml/1¼pts skimmed milk
- 2 tbsp ground flax seeds
- 2 tsp instant coffee

Method

1 First, place the oats in a food processor and blend until fine.

2 Slice the banana into small chunks and add to the blender.

3 Dissolve the coffee in 2 tablespoons of boiling water and add to the blender.

4 Add the other ingredients and blitz.

5 Adjust the Stevia to taste, then pour into a glass and serve.

FROM YOUR STORE CUPBOARD
Stevia to taste

COCONUT FLOUR LOW CARB PANCAKES

Nutrition Facts
Per Serving
Calories 158
Total Carbs 3g
Net Carbs 2g

5 Ingredients

- 4 eggs
- 1 tbsp coconut oil, melted
- 60ml/2floz almond milk
- 60ml/2floz coconut cream, melted
- 3 tbsp coconut flour

Method

1 Place all the ingredients together in a large mixing bowl.

2 Mix with an electric whisk until the batter is smooth and lump free.

3 Set the batter aside for 10 minutes.

4 Brush a small 15cm/6-inch frying pan lightly with oil and heat over a medium-high heat.

5 Pour ¼ of the batter into the pan and tilt the pan to spread out the batter.

6 Cook for around 3 minutes until the sides are dry and crispy and you can flip the pancake over.

7 Brown on the other side for a further 2 minutes and remove from the pan.

8 Serve with your favourite fillings such as yoghurt, sliced almonds, sugar-free jam, cream cheese, fresh berries, and sugar-free chocolate chips.

FROM YOUR STORE CUPBOARD
½ tsp vanilla extract

QUINOA HAZELNUT PORRIDGE

Nutrition Facts
Per Serving
Calories 235
Total Carbs 45g
Net Carbs 38g

5 Ingredients

- 200g/7oz quinoa
- 360ml/12½oz skimmed milk
- 1 red apple, chopped

- 1 tbsp sultanas
- 75g/3oz hazelnuts, finely chopped

Method

1 Put the quinoa, water, and cinnamon in a heavy-based saucepan and bring to the boil.

2 Reduce the heat and simmer for 15 minutes.

3 Stir in the apple, sultanas, and milk and simmer for a further 5 minutes.

4 Top with the hazelnuts and serve immediately.

FROM YOUR STORE CUPBOARD
750ml/1¼pts water
1 tsp cinnamon

AVOCADO & EGGS ON TOAST

Nutrition Facts
Per Serving
Calories 240
Total Carbs 25g
Net Carbs 16g

5 Ingredients

- 4 eggs
- 4 slices of whole grain bread
- 1 avocado
- 4 tbsp low-fat Greek yoghurt

Method

1 Halve and stone the avocado.

2 Scoop out the filling and mash in a bowl.

3 Poach the eggs in a large pan of boiling water for 3-5 minutes, depending on your taste.

4 Toast the bread and spread with the mashed avocado.

5 Top the avocado toast with a poached egg and a spoonful of Greek yoghurt.

6 Season with salt and pepper and serve immediately.

FROM YOUR STORE CUPBOARD
Salt and pepper

ITALIAN STYLE SPAGHETTI SQUASH

Nutrition Facts
Per Serving
Calories 140
Total Carbs 16g
Net Carbs 14g

5 Ingredients

- 1 675g/1½lb spaghetti squash
- 175g/6oz lean ham
- 450ml/15½floz tomato pasta sauce

- 40g/1½oz Parmesan cheese, grated
- 2 tsp fresh oregano, chopped

Method

1 Preheat the oven to 375F/190C/Gas Mark 5.

2 Spray a pan with cooking spray and lay the squash in the pan with the cut side facing downwards.

3 Bake for 45 minutes.

4 Remove the squash from the oven and use a fork to remove spaghetti strands of squash flesh.

5 Mix the spaghetti with the tomato sauce, ham, pepper, and oregano.

6 Pile the filling back into the squash shell and top with Parmesan.

7 Return to the oven and bake for 25 minutes or until golden brown.

8 To serve cut each half into two.

FROM YOUR STORE CUPBOARD
Cooking spray
Pepper

QUICK CHICKEN CURRIED COUSCOUS

Nutrition Facts
Per Serving
Calories 273
Total Carbs 39g
Net Carbs 35g

5 Ingredients

- 2 tsp butter
- 300g/11oz chicken breasts, cut into strips
- 300g/11oz frozen vegetables of your choice
- 125g/4oz Indian spiced-flavoured couscous mix
- 50g/2oz raisins

Method

1 Heat the butter in a large non-stick frying pan until melted.

2 Add the chicken and cook for 3 minutes.

3 Now add the water and vegetables and bring to the boil.

4 Finally, add the couscous and raisins and remove from the heat.

5 Cover the pan and leave for 5 minutes for the couscous to absorb the liquid.

6 Stir the couscous well and fluff with a fork before serving.

FROM YOUR STORE CUPBOARD
250ml/8½floz boiling water

CRUSTLESS CHEDDAR & BROCCOLI QUICHE

Nutrition Facts
Per Serving
Calories 300
Total Carbs 15g
Net Carbs 11g

5 Ingredients

- 1 small red onion, halved and thinly sliced
- 150g/5oz broccoli florets, finely chopped
- 4 large eggs
- 450ml/15½floz whole milk
- 125g/4oz mature cheddar cheese, grated

Method

1 Preheat the oven to 400F/200C/Gas Mark 6.

2 Spray a deep pie dish with cooking spray.

3 Heat the oil in a pan and fry the onion until soft, for around 5 minutes.

4 Add the broccoli and fry for a further 10 minutes or until it begins to brown.

5 Make the quiche custard by beating together the eggs and milk.

6 Add the cheese and season with salt and pepper.

7 Transfer the cooled broccoli mixture into the pie dish and pour over the custard.

8 Bake in the oven for 30-40 minutes until the quiche is puffed up and golden.

9 Serve warm or cold with a salad.

FROM YOUR STORE CUPBOARD
Cooking spray
2 tbsp olive oil
Salt and pepper

PORK & PEPPER PITTAS

Nutrition Facts
Per Serving
Calories 380
Total Carbs 37g
Net Carbs 35g

5 Ingredients

- 450g/1lb boneless pork loin chops, cut into thin strips
- 350g/12oz roasted sweet red bell peppers, drained and cut into strips
- 4 wholemeal pitta bread
- 25g/1oz lettuce, shredded

Method

1 Mix the pork together with the oil, garlic, salt and pepper in a bowl.

2 Heat a frying pan to a medium high heat.

3 Brown the pork strips for a few minutes until cooked through.

4 Now add the red peppers and cook for a further 3 minutes.

5 Warm the pitta bread in the toaster and then split each open.

6 Fill the pitta pockets with lettuce and then the pork mixture.

7 Serve with low-cal garlic mayonnaise if desired.

FROM YOUR STORE CUPBOARD
1 tbsp olive oil
2 garlic cloves, crushed
Sat and pepper

DIABETES
Type 2
HEALING
CODE

PROSCIUTTO WRAPPED CHICKEN

Nutrition Facts
Per Serving
Calories 294
Total Carbs 2g
Net Carbs 2g

5 Ingredients

- 2 chicken breasts
- 75g/3oz finely sliced prosciutto or Parma ham
- 60g/2½oz low-fat cream cheese
- 10-20 fresh basil leaves

Method

1 Preheat the oven to 375F/190C/Gas Mark 5.

2 Lay the slices of prosciutto out onto the tin foil so the edges overlap a little.

3 Now spread the cream cheese over the prosciutto.

4 Top with a covering of basil leaves.

5 Season the chicken breasts with pepper, and gently wrap the prosciutto around the chicken.

6 Bake in the oven for 25-30 minutes.

7 Perfect served with green vegetables.

FROM YOUR STORE CUPBOARD
Pepper

HEALTHY STUFFED CHICKEN BREAST

Nutrition Facts
Per Serving
Calories 262
Total Carbs 8g
Net Carbs 6g

5 Ingredients

- 2 chicken breasts
- 50g/2oz low-fat mozzarella, diced
- 2 canned artichoke hearts, chopped
- 2 tsp sundried tomatoes, chopped
- 10 basil leaves, chopped

Method

1 Preheat oven to 375F/190C/Gas Mark 5.

2 Cut the chicken breasts through the middle to make a large pocket.

3 Mix all the other ingredients together in a small bowl.

4 Use the stuffing to fill the chicken pocket and secure with cocktail sticks along the open side.

5 Place the stuffed chicken breasts onto a baking tray and season with paprika and pepper.

6 Bake for approximately 20 - 25 minutes.

7 It's up to you if you remove the cocktail sticks or just let people know there are cocktail sticks in there!

FROM YOUR STORE CUPBOARD

2 garlic cloves, crushed
¼ tsp paprika powder
Pepper
Cocktail sticks

ROASTED TOMATO AND BALSAMIC CHICKEN

SERVES 4

Nutrition Facts
Per Serving
Calories 306
Total Carbs 16g
Net Carbs 15g

5 Ingredients

- 4 175g/6oz boneless skinless chicken breasts
- 2 tbsp honey
- 400g/14oz grape or cherry tomatoes
- 2 tbsp balsamic glaze

Method

1 Preheat the oven to 400F/200C/Gas Mark 6.

2 Mix 1 tablespoon of olive oil with the honey in a medium bowl.

3 Coat the tomatoes in the honey and oil then arrange in a baking dish.

4 Bake the tomatoes for around 5 minutes or until beginning to soften.

5 Use a rolling pin or meat tenderizer to flatten the chicken breasts until around 1cm or ½inch thick.

6 Season the chicken breasts and shallow fry them in the remaining olive oil.

7 Serve the chicken immediately with the tomatoes and balsamic glaze.

FROM YOUR STORE CUPBOARD
2 tbsp olive oil
Salt and pepper

CHICKEN WITH BAKED TOMATOES

Nutrition Facts
Per Serving
Calories 373
Total Carbs 27g
Net Carbs 13g

5 Ingredients

- 600g/1lb5oz chicken breast
- 4 large corn cobs
- 2 tbsp coriander seeds
- 250g/9oz cherry tomatoes

Method

1 Remove the corn kernels from the cobs and steam the corn for around 4 minutes.

2 Put the corn in a blender and blitz with a little of the steaming water from the pan to make a smooth puree.

3 Slice the chicken breasts in half and fry in a non-stick pan with a little water, for around 4 minutes each side.

4 At the end of the cooking time add the coriander seeds and pepper to the frying pan and coat the chicken well.

5 Remove the chicken and keep warm.

6 Add the tomatoes to the pan and cook until they are beginning to soften.

7 Serve the chicken on a bed of sweetcorn puree with the tomatoes.

FROM YOUR STORE CUPBOARD
Pepper

37

BALSAMIC CHICKEN WITH MUSHROOMS

Nutrition Facts
Per Serving
Calories 240
Total Carbs 12g
Net Carbs 11g

5 Ingredients

- 450g/1lb chicken breasts
- 1 tbsp margarine
- 300g/11oz button mushrooms, sliced
- 5 tbsp balsamic vinegar

Method

1 Use a meat mallet or tenderiser to flatten the chicken breasts.

2 Coat the chicken pieces in the flour.

3 Heat the oil in a large heavy-based frying pan and add the chicken.

4 Fry the chicken on 3-5 minutes, each side until cooked. Set aside.

5 Now add the margarine and mushrooms to the pan and cook for 5 minutes.

6 Add the balsamic vinegar and bring to the boil.

7 Prepare the stock with the stock cube and boiling water, and add to the pan.

8 Simmer to reduce the liquid for 5 minutes.

9 Add the chicken back to the pan and simmer for 2 more minutes.

10 Season with pepper before serving

FROM YOUR STORE CUPBOARD

½ chicken stock cube
200ml/7floz boiling water
1 tbsp olive oil
50g/2oz plain flour
Pepper

APPLE & THYME GLAZED CHICKEN THIGHS

Nutrition Facts
Per Serving
Calories 204
Total Carbs 4g
Net Carbs 4g

5 Ingredients

- 4 175g/6oz boneless skinless chicken thighs
- 175ml/6floz unsweetened apple juice
- 1 tsp fresh thyme, chopped

Method

1 Season the chicken thighs with salt and pepper.

2 Heat the oil in a large heavy-based frying pan and brown the chicken on each side for 5 minutes. Set aside.

3 Add the apple juice and thyme to the pan and bring to the boil.

4 Continue to boil until the liquid has reduced by half.

5 Return the chicken to the pan and continue to cook for a further 5 minutes.

6 Serve immediately with lots of steamed vegetables.

FROM YOUR STORE CUPBOARD
1 tbsp vegetable oil
Salt and pepper

MEXICAN BEEF WITH COURGETTES

Nutrition Facts

Per Serving

Calories 272

Total Carbs 6g

Net Carbs 4g

5 Ingredients

- 450g/1lb lean minced/ground beef
- 225g/8oz canned Mexican-style diced tomatoes
- ½ tsp onion powder
- ¼ tsp crushed red pepper flakes
- 2 small courgettes/zucchinis, sliced and quartered

Method

1 First season the beef with salt and pepper.

2 Brown the mince in a frying pan along with the crushed garlic.

3 Now add the tomatoes and spices.

4 Cover the pan and simmer on a low heat for a further 10 minutes.

5 Add the courgettes and cover the pan again. Cook for an additional 10 minutes or until the courgette is tender but firm.

6 You can serve this dish with a small portion of brown rice.

FROM YOUR STORE CUPBOARD

2 tsp chilli powder

1 tsp ground cumin

2 garlic cloves, crushed

Salt and pepper to taste

MARINATED STEAK AND BROCCOLI

Nutrition Facts
Per Serving
Calories 309
Total Carbs 13g
Net Carbs 10g

5 Ingredients

- 225g/8oz lean beef, sliced into thin strips
- 225g/8oz broccoli florets

Method

1 Make a marinade by mixing together the soy sauce, balsamic vinegar, olive oil, and pepper.

2 Place the marinade and steak in a bag and leave in the fridge for at least an hour but preferably overnight.

3 Heat a large wok and fry the steak and marinade together in the pan, along with the broccoli florets.

4 You can cook for 2-4 minutes depending on your taste.

5 Serve immediately with a small portion of brown rice.

FROM YOUR STORE CUPBOARD

2 tsp soy sauce
2 tsp balsamic vinegar
2 tsp olive oil
Pepper

BEEF FAJITAS

Nutrition Facts
Per Serving
Calories 336
Total Carbs 7g
Net Carbs 3g

5 Ingredients

- 450g/1lb lean beef, sliced into thin strips
- 1 medium red onion, sliced
- 1 red bell pepper, sliced
- 1 yellow bell pepper, sliced

Method

1 Heat a large wok and add the oil.

2 Season the beef and cook for 2-3 minutes. Set the beef aside.

3 Add the onions, peppers, cumin and chilli powder to the wok and cook for 2 minutes.

4 Now quickly return the beef to the wok for 30 seconds, and serve immediately.

5 Ideal served with sliced avocado, lemon juice, and freshly chopped coriander/cilantro

FROM YOUR STORE CUPBOARD

½ tsp cumin
½ tsp chilli powder
1 tsp olive oil
Salt and pepper

BEEF IN RED WINE AND MUSHROOM SAUCE

Nutrition Facts
Per Serving
Calories 266
Total Carbs 4g
Net Carbs 3g

5 Ingredients

- 24 125g/4oz beef tenderloin steaks, trimmed to 1cm/½-inch thickness
- 225g/8oz portobello mushrooms, sliced
- 250ml/8½floz dry red wine
- 25g/1oz butter
- 1 tsp fresh rosemary, chopped

Method

1 Heat the oil in a large frying pan and add the seasoned steak strips.

2 Heat over a medium-high heat for 4-5 minutes then keep warm on a plate.

3 Add the mushrooms to the pan and fry for 3 minutes.

4 Now add the wine and cook until the liquid has reduced by half.

5 Add the butter and rosemary and stir until the butter has melted.

6 Pour the sauce over the steak and serve.

FROM YOUR STORE CUPBOARD
1 tbsp olive oil
Salt and pepper

BEEF AND VEGETABLE PIE

Nutrition Facts
Per Serving
Calories 330
Total Carbs 30g
Net Carbs 23g

5 Ingredients

- 500g/1lb2oz lean minced/ground beef
- 150g/5oz onion
- 450g/1lb frozen carrot, peas, and sweetcorn
- 175g/6oz courgette/zucchini, grated
- 14 sheets of filo pastry

Method

1 Brown the mince in a non-stick frying pan. Add the onion to the pan and continue to dry fry for a further 2 minutes.

2 Add the frozen vegetables and courgette and continue to cook for a further 2 minutes.

3 Prepare the stock with the stock cube and boiling water, and add to the pan. Bring to the boil and simmer for a further 5 minutes.

4 Mix the gravy powder with the water and add to the pan along with the Worcestershire sauce and tomato ketchup. Simmer for 2 minutes until the gravy had thickened, then leave to cool.

5 Spray a 20cm/8-inch pie dish with cooking spray and use 8 pieces of filo pastry to line the dish.

6 Spoon in the filling and use the remaining 6 sheets of filo pastry to make a lid for the pie. Spray with cooking spray as you work with the filo pastry.

7 Make a slit in the pastry lid before baking for 30-35 minutes until golden brown. Serve immediately.

FROM YOUR STORE CUPBOARD

1 vegetable stock cube
450ml/15½floz boiling water
and 5 tbsp water extra
1 tbsp tomato ketchup
1 tsp Worcestershire sauce
3 tbsp gravy powder
Pepper

GINGER PORK TENDERLOIN

Nutrition Facts
Per Serving
Calories 181
Total Carbs 3g
Net Carbs 3g

5 Ingredients

- 450g/1lb pork tenderloin, cut into thick strips
- 1 tbsp peanut oil
- 1 tbsp honey
- 1 tbsp fresh ginger, grated

Method

1 Place all the ingredients except the oil in a large resealable bag.

2 Seal the bag and shake the ingredients to mix.

3 Leave the pork to marinade in the fridge for an hour.

4 Heat the peanut oil in a large frying pan and fry the pork and marinade together for around 5 minutes.

5 Serve immediately, ideally with sweet potato wedges and green vegetables.

FROM YOUR STORE CUPBOARD
2 tsp olive oil
2 tsp light soy sauce
2 garlic cloves, crushed

PORK TENDERLOIN WITH LIGHT MUSTARD SAUCE

5 Ingredients

- 450g/1lb pork tenderloin, cut into 2½cm/1-inch pieces
- 60ml/2floz single cream
- 2 tbsp Dijon mustard

Method

1 Season the pork pieces, then place them between 2 sheets of clingfilm.

2 Flatten with a meat tenderiser or a rolling pin until ½cm/¼inch thick.

3 Heat the oil in a frying pan and cook the pork for 2 minutes on each side.

4 Reduce the heat, then add the cream and mustard.

5 Simmer for 2 minutes, then serve the pork with the sauce.

6 Ideal served with balsamic glazed asparagus.

FROM YOUR STORE CUPBOARD

1 tbsp vegetable oil
Salt and pepper

46

POLYNESIAN PORK

Nutrition Facts
Per Serving
Calories 298
Total Carbs 38g
Net Carbs 35g

5 Ingredients

- 225g/8oz pork tenderloin, cut into small chunks
- 375g/13oz canned pineapple in juice, drained with juice reserved
- 50g/2oz sliced water chestnuts, drained
- 50g/2oz broccoli florets
- ½ red bell pepper, chopped

Method

1 Heat the oil in a wok and fry the pork for 5 minutes.

2 Now add the pineapple and vegetables to the pan and continue to cook for 1 minute.

3 Combine the reserved pineapple juice and the remaining ingredients in a small bowl and mix well.

4 Add the marinade and cook for 3-5 minutes, according to taste.

5 Serve immediately.

FROM YOUR STORE CUPBOARD

1 tsp vegetable oil
2 tsp light soy sauce
1 tsp white wine vinegar
1 tsp tomato ketchup
2 tsp corn flour
2 tsp granulated Stevia

PORK CHOPS WITH BUTTERNUT SQUASH

SERVES 4

Nutrition Facts
Per Serving
Calories 267
Total Carbs 18g
Net Carbs 15g

5 Ingredients

- 4 125g/4oz boneless loin pork chops
- 550g/1¼lb butternut squash, chopped
- 1 medium onion, chopped
- 4 tbsp water
- 1 tbsp fresh mint, chopped

Method

1 Season the pork generously with salt and pepper.

2 Heat the oil in a large frying pan and cook for 3-4 minutes each side. Keep warm on a serving plate.

3 Add the squash to the frying pan and cook for around 7 minutes.

4 Add the onion and cook for a further 5 minutes.

5 Add the water and continue to cook until the water has evaporated.

6 Serve the squash with the pork and garnish with the mint.

FROM YOUR STORE CUPBOARD
1 tbsp olive oil
Salt and pepper

48

ORANGE AND BALSAMIC LAMB

Nutrition Facts
Per Serving
Calories 226
Total Carbs 2g
Net Carbs 2g

5 Ingredients

- 8 125g/4oz lean lamb chops, trimmed
- 2 tsp grated orange rind
- 1 tbsp fresh orange juice
- 3 tablespoons balsamic vinegar

Method

1 Mix the orange juice, balsamic vinegar and orange rind with 1 tablespoon of oil in a sealable plastic bag. Add the lamb to the bag and leave to marinade at room temperature for 10 minutes.

2 Remove the lamb from the bag and season with salt and pepper.

3 Heat a large frying pan and cook the lamb with the marinade for approximately 2 minutes on each side.

4 Serve the lamb with the syrupy marinade and drizzle with the remaining 1 teaspoon of olive oil.

5 Perfect served with steamed broccoli.

FROM YOUR STORE CUPBOARD
2 tsp olive oil, divided
Salt and pepper

LAMB CUTLETS WITH HAZELNUTS

Nutrition Facts
Per Serving
Calories 488
Total Carbs 55g
Net Carbs 45g

5 Ingredients

- 4 sweet potatoes, sliced into 1cm/½-inch pieces
- 1 bunch asparagus
- 8 lamb cutlets
- 75g/3oz hazelnuts
- 75g/3oz rocket

Method

1 Boil the potatoes until tender.

2 Steam the asparagus until tender and set aside with the potatoes.

3 Spray the cutlets with the cooking spray and sprinkle with paprika.

4 Grill the cutlets for 2-3 each side.

5 Mix the vinegar, oil, and mustard together.

6 Toss the lamb, potatoes, asparagus, and hazelnuts in the dressing and serve immediately.

FROM YOUR STORE CUPBOARD
Cooking spray
2 tbsp red wine vinegar
2 tbsp wholegrain mustard
1 tbsp olive oil
1 tsp paprika

HERB CRUSTED LAMB

Nutrition Facts
Per Serving
Calories 231
Total Carbs 0g
Net Carbs 0g

5 Ingredients

- 8 75g/3oz lamb loin chops
- 3 tbsp Dijon mustard

- 1 tbsp fresh rosemary, chopped
- 1 tbsp fresh thyme, chopped

Method

1 Season the lamb chops well with salt and pepper.

2 Mix the garlic cloves into the mustard along with the fresh herbs.

3 Grill the chops on one side for 6 minutes under a medium-high grill setting.

4 Turn the chops and brush with the herb mixture.

5 Grill the lamb for a further 6-8 minutes depending on if you prefer your lamb pink or more well done.

6 Perfect served with steamed spring greens.

FROM YOUR STORE CUPBOARD
Salt and pepper
3 garlic cloves, crushed

FRESH SALMON SPAGHETTI

Nutrition Facts
Per Serving
Calories 487
Total Carbs 41g
Net Carbs 34g

5 Ingredients

- 4 eggs
- 200g/7oz salmon fillets, thinly sliced
- 25g/1oz baby spinach leaves
- 1 lemon, zested and juiced
- 25g/1oz parmesan cheese, shaved

Method

1 Cook the pasta in a large pan of boiling water until al dente.

2 Drain the pasta leaving a little of the water and place in a large bowl.

3 Add the salmon and spinach leaves and stir through for 2 minutes, allowing the heat from the pasta to cook the salmon and wilt the spinach leaves.

4 Combine the oil, pepper, lemon juice, and zest together, then toss through the pasta.

5 Carefully poach the eggs in a large pan of boiling water.

6 Serve the pasta in serving bowls topped with a poached egg and shavings of parmesan.

FROM YOUR STORE CUPBOARD
275g/10oz whole wheat spaghetti, cooked to al dente and drained
50ml/2floz olive oil
Pepper

BAKED PLAICE WITH DIJON THYME TOPPING

Nutrition Facts
Per Serving
Calories 140
Total Carbs 0g
Net Carbs 0g

5 Ingredients

- 2 175g/6oz plaice fillets
- 2 tbsp fresh parsley
- 1 tbsp reduced-fat margarine
- 1 tsp Dijon mustard

Method

1 Preheat the oven to 350F/180C/Gas Mark 4.

2 Spray a baking sheet with a light film of cooking spray.

3 Place the fish on the baking tray.

4 Mix all the remaining ingredients together well in a small bowl and spread over the plaice.

5 Bake in the oven for 12-15 minutes.

6 Serve garnished with chopped fresh parsley if desired.

FROM YOUR STORE CUPBOARD
Cooking spray
1 tsp dried thyme
Salt and pepper

GARLIC BUTTER BAKED SALMON

Nutrition Facts
Per Serving
Calories 350
Total Carbs 2g
Net Carbs 2g

5 Ingredients

- 50g/2oz unsalted butter
- 2 tbsp parsley, finely chopped
- 3 tbsp freshly squeezed lemon juice
- 4 salmon fillets

Method

1 Preheat the oven to 400F/200C/Gas Mark 6.

2 Line a baking tray with tin foil.

3 Clean the salmon and remove any visible bones with tweezers.

4 Melt the butter in a small bowl in the microwave.

5 Add the garlic, salt and pepper, and lemon juice to the butter and mix well.

6 Brush the salmon fillets with the garlic butter using a pastry brush.

7 Bake the fillets for 12 - 18 minutes. (Thicker salmon fillets will require longer cooking time).

8 If desired, drizzle with lemon juice and garnish with chopped parsley.

FROM YOUR STORE CUPBOARD
2 garlic cloves, crushed
Salt and pepper to taste

BAKED COD WITH SICILIAN TOMATO PESTO

Nutrition Facts
Per Serving
Calories 280
Total Carbs 7g
Net Carbs 6g

Ingredients

- 4 175g/6oz cod fillets
- 1 bunch of basil
- 2 tbsp pine nuts

- 25g/1oz Parmigiano-Reggiano cheese
- 2 medium tomatoes, chopped

Method

1 Preheat the oven to 375F/190C/Gas Mark 5.

2 Make the pesto by blitzing the basil leaves, pine nuts, garlic, oil and parmesan in a mini food processor.

3 Spray a baking tray with cooking spray.

4 Arrange the fish on the tray and season with salt and pepper.

5 Cook for around 15 minutes.

6 Mix the pesto with the tomato and a pinch of salt and pepper.

7 Serve the fish topped with the tomato pesto.

FROM YOUR STORE CUPBOARD

4 tsp olive oil
2 garlic cloves
Salt and pepper
Cooking spray

SALMON & PRAWN FUSILLI

Nutrition Facts
Per Serving
Calories 349
Total Carbs 32g
Net Carbs 27g

Ingredients

- 60g/2½oz salmon
- 60g/2½oz cooked prawns
- 40g/1½oz whole wheat pasta
- 2 tbsp reduced fat crème fraîche/sour cream
- 1 tbsp fresh dill

Method

1 Preheat the oven to 400F/200C/Gas Mark 6.

2 Cook the salmon for 15 minutes.

3 Remove the skin and flake the fish.

4 Cook the pasta in boiling water until al dente.

5 Drain the pasta and return to the pan.

6 Stir the salmon, prawns, crème fraîche, dill, and pepper through the pasta.

7 Serve immediately.

FROM YOUR STORE CUPBOARD
Pepper

DIABETES *Type 2* HEALING CODE

SIDES

LOW-CARB ROASTED CAULIFLOWER MASH

Nutrition Facts
Per Serving
Calories 188
Total Carbs 13g
Net Carbs 7g

Ingredients

- 900g/2lb cauliflower, cut into florets
- 40g/1½oz unsalted butter
- 3 tbsp crème fraîche/sour cream

Method

1 Preheat the oven to 350F/180C/Gas Mark 4.

2 Arrange the cauliflower florets on a large baking tray.

3 Now drizzle the olive oil all over and use your hands to massage the oil into the florets.

4 Sprinkle with oregano and continue to use your hands to make sure the oregano is evenly distributed.

5 Bake in the oven for 25-30 minutes. It's done when it's just starting to turn brown.

6 Turn the cauliflower out into a food processor and add the butter, crème fraîche, and garlic.

7 Blitz the mash for 2-4 minutes to make sure it's velvety smooth. Use a spatula to clean down the sides of the bowl and blitz again.

8 Season to taste with salt and pepper.

9 Garnish with chives, parsley, and chilli flakes if desired.

FROM YOUR STORE CUPBOARD

4 garlic cloves, crushed
Salt and pepper to taste
2 tbsp olive oil
1 tsp oregano

HARVEST SWEET POTATO WEDGES

Nutrition Facts
Per Serving
Calories 97
Total Carbs 13g
Net Carbs 11g

Ingredients

- 1 300g/11oz sweet potato, peeled

Method

1 Preheat the oven to 425F/220C/Gas Mark 7.

2 Coat a baking tray with cooking spray.

3 Slice the sweet potato into 8 wedges.

4 Mix the allspice, salt, and oil together in a bowl.

5 Toss the wedges in the oil, then arrange on the baking tray.

6 Bake the wedges for around 15 minutes. Then turn the wedges and bake for a further 15 minutes or until golden.

7 Ideal served with meat and fish.

FROM YOUR STORE CUPBOARD

2 tsp vegetable oil
½ tsp mixed allspice
Cooking spray
Salt

SERVES 2

BALSAMIC ROASTED ASPARAGUS

Nutrition Facts
Per Serving
Calories 60
Total Carbs 4g
Net Carbs 2g

Ingredients

- 150g/5oz asparagus, trimmed
- 2 tsp balsamic vinegar

Method

1 Preheat the oven to 350F/180C/Gas Mark 4.

2 Place the asparagus on to a sheet of aluminium foil.

3 Drizzle the balsamic vinegar and oil over the asparagus and season with salt and pepper.

4 Seal the parcel by bringing the edges of the foil together and place on a baking tray.

5 Roast the asparagus for around 15 minutes or until tender.

FROM YOUR STORE CUPBOARD
2 tsp olive oil
Salt and pepper

ROASTED CHILLI CORN

Nutrition Facts
Per Serving
Calories 141
Total Carbs 17g
Net Carbs 15g

Ingredients

- 4 corn on the cob, husked
- 2 tsp fresh coriander/cilantro, chopped

Method

1 Preheat the oven to 425F/220C/Gas Mark 7.

2 In a small bowl, mix the oil, garlic, chilli powder, coriander, salt, and pepper.

3 Place each corn on the cob on an individual sheet of aluminium foil.

4 Brush the corn with the oil and seal the parcels.

5 Roast for around 25 minutes until the corn is tender.

6 Serve immediately.

FROM YOUR STORE CUPBOARD

1 garlic clove, crushed
2 tbsp olive oil
¼ tsp chilli powder
Salt and pepper

HERBY LEMON CAULIFLOWER

SERVES 4

Nutrition Facts
Per Serving
Calories 161
Total Carbs 8g
Net Carbs 5g

Ingredients

- 1 medium cauliflower, cut into florets
- Zest and juice of 1 lemon
- 3 tbsp fresh parsley, chopped
- 1 tbsp fresh rosemary, chopped
- 1 tbsp fresh thyme, chopped

Method

1 Preheat the oven to 425F/220C/Gas Mark 7.

2 Place the cauliflower on a baking tray drizzled with 2 tablespoons of oil.

3 Bake the cauliflower for approximately 20 minutes or until golden and tender.

4 Combine the remaining oil with the herbs and lemon juice and zest in a large bowl.

5 Add the cauliflower, toss well and serve immediately.

FROM YOUR STORE CUPBOARD
4 tbsp olive oil
¼ tsp crushed red pepper flakes
Salt

SERVES 4

CAULIFLOWER RICE

Nutrition Facts
Per Serving
Calories 59
Total Carbs 8g
Net Carbs 5g

Ingredients

- 1 large cauliflower, cut into pieces

Method

1 Preheat the oven to 450F/230C/Gas Mark 8.

2 Line a large baking tray with foil and spray with cooking spray.

3 Pulse the cauliflower pieces in a food processor until you have small pieces that look like rice grains.

4 Transfer the rice to a bowl and toss in salt and pepper and oil.

5 Arrange a layer of rice on the baking tray and bake for 15 minutes.

6 Turn the rice and roast again for a further 5 minutes.

7 Continue roasting and turning until the rice is brown.

8 Serve immediately.

FROM YOUR STORE CUPBOARD
Cooking spray
2 tsp olive oil
Salt and pepper

63

ASPARAGUS & PEPPER SIDE

SERVES 4

Nutrition Facts
Per Serving
Calories 50
Total Carbs 5g
Net Carbs 4g

Ingredients

- 225g/8oz asparagus, trimmed and cut into pieces
- 1 small red onion, sliced
- 125g/4oz mushrooms, sliced
- ½ medium red bell pepper, diced

Method

1 Heat the oil in a wok over a medium to high heat.

2 Add the asparagus and onion to the pan and cook for 10 minutes.

3 Add the mushrooms and red pepper and cook for a further 5 minutes.

4 Now add the garlic and cook for a final minute.

5 Season with salt and pepper and serve immediately.

FROM YOUR STORE CUPBOARD
1 tbsp olive oil
1 garlic clove, crushed
Salt and pepper

PARMESAN & ALMOND BROCCOLI

Nutrition Facts
Per Serving
Calories 110
Total Carbs 6g
Net Carbs 3g

Ingredients

- 350g/12oz broccoli florets
- 3 tbsp slivered almonds
- 1 tbsp lemon juice
- 1 tbsp Parmesan cheese, grated

Method

1 Preheat the oven to 425F/220C/Gas Mark 7.

2 Lightly spray a baking tray with cooking spray.

3 Mix the broccoli, oil, almonds, and garlic together with some pepper in a bowl.

4 Arrange the broccoli on the baking tray and bake for around 10 minutes or until beginning to brown.

5 Pour the broccoli into a bowl and toss with the lemon juice and parmesan.

6 Serve immediately.

FROM YOUR STORE CUPBOARD
Cooking spray,
1 tbsp olive oil
2 garlic cloves, minced
Pepper

GARLICKY KALE & SPINACH

Nutrition Facts
Per Serving
Calories 90
Total Carbs 8g
Net Carbs 6g

Ingredients

- 300g/11oz baby spinach
- 200g/7oz kale, chopped

Method

1 Begin by heating the oil in a large heavy-based pan.

2 Add the garlic and fry for 1 minute.

3 Now add the kale, spinach and apple cider vinegar and mix well.

4 Reduce the heat and cook for around 5-7 minutes.

5 Season and serve immediately with meat, chicken or fish.

FROM YOUR STORE CUPBOARD

1 tbsp apple cider vinegar
3 garlic cloves, crushed
4 tsp olive oil
Salt and pepper

TASTY BRUSSELS WITH CRANBERRIES

Nutrition Facts
Per Serving
Calories 80
Total Carbs 10g
Net Carbs 8g

Ingredients

- 225g/8oz Brussels sprouts, trimmed and halved
- 2 tbsp dried cranberries

Method

1 Preheat the oven to 400F/200C/Gas Mark 6.

2 Spray a thin film of oil over the tray using the cooking spray.

3 Mix all the ingredients together in a bowl.

4 Pour the mixture onto the baking tray.

5 Bake for 10 minutes then turn and toss the sprouts.

6 Bake for a further 10-15 minutes or until just brown

FROM YOUR STORE CUPBOARD
Cooking spray
1 tbsp olive oil
1 tbsp balsamic vinegar
Salt and pepper

ROASTED AUTUMN VEGETABLES

Nutrition Facts
Per Serving
Calories 60
Total Carbs 6g
Net Carbs 4g

Ingredients

- 150g/5oz cauliflower florets
- 150g/5oz Brussels sprouts, trimmed and halved
- 50g/2oz baby carrots

Method

1 Preheat the oven to 400F/200C/Gas Mark 6.

2 Lightly grease a baking tray with oil using the cooking spray.

3 Mix all the ingredients together in a large bowl.

4 Spread the vegetables in a layer on the baking tray.

5 Bake for 25 minutes or until the vegetables are tender.

FROM YOUR STORE CUPBOARD
Cooking spray
1 tbsp olive oil
Salt and pepper

BRAISED FENNEL AND WHITE BEANS

Nutrition Facts
Per Serving
Calories 170
Total Carbs 26g
Net Carbs 18g

Ingredients

- 2 300g/11oz medium fennel bulbs, stems removed, cut into eight
- 2 medium onions, peeled and quartered
- 1 400g/14oz can of cannellini beans, drained and rinsed
- 2 tbsp red wine vinegar
- 1 tbsp fresh parsley, chopped

Method

1 Preheat the oven to 375F/190C/Gas Mark 5.

2 Spray a large baking dish with cooking spray.

3 Arrange the fennel and onion in the baking dish, and season with salt and pepper.

4 Prepare the stock with the boiling water and stock cube, and pour over the vegetables.

5 Pour the oil and vinegar over the vegetables before baking for 1 hour, stirring midway through the cooking.

6 Now add the beans and fresh parsley, and return to the oven for a final 15 minutes.

FROM YOUR STORE CUPBOARD
Cooking spray
½ chicken stock cube
250ml/8½floz boiling water
1 tbsp olive oil
Salt and pepper

ROASTED RED POTATOES AND GREEN BEANS

Nutrition Facts
Per Serving
Calories 175
Total Carbs 24g
Net Carbs 20g

Ingredients

- 450g/1lb green beans
- 6 baby red potatoes, cut into pieces

Method

1 Preheat the oven to 400F/200C/Gas Mark 6.

2 Spray a baking tray with cooking spray.

3 In a bowl, mix the potatoes well with 1 tablespoon of oil, as well as the parsley and pepper.

4 Arrange the potatoes in a layer on the baking tray and bake for 15 minutes.

5 In a bowl, mix the green beans with the remaining oil and garlic salt.

6 Add the green beans to the tray and cook for a further 20 minutes or until the potatoes are tender and brown.

7 Serve immediately.

FROM YOUR STORE CUPBOARD

Cooking spray
2 tbsp olive oil
½ tsp garlic salt
¼ tsp dried parsley
Pepper

COUSCOUS, COURGETTE & TOMATO SALAD

Nutrition Facts

Per Serving

Calories 197

Total Carbs 38g

Net Carbs 31g

Ingredients

- 1 small onion, thinly sliced and separated into rings
- 350g/12oz courgette/zucchini, cut into 1cm/½-inch-thick wedges
- 2 tsp fresh thyme, chopped
- 15g/5oz cherry tomatoes, halved
- 125g/4oz whole-wheat couscous

Method

1 Heat the oil in a large heavy-based saucepan.

2 Fry the garlic and onion for around 5 minutes until soft and fragrant.

3 Prepare the stock with the stock cube and boiling water.

4 Add the stock, salt, thyme, and the courgettes to the pan.

5 Bring to the boil and cook for 3 minutes.

6 Now add the tomatoes and the couscous and remove from the heat.

7 Cover the pan with a lid and leave for 5 minutes to allow the couscous to absorb the liquid.

8 Stir well and fluff with a fork before serving.

FROM YOUR STORE CUPBOARD

1 garlic clove, crushed

1 tsp olive oil

¾ chicken stock cube

300ml/10½floz boiling water

Salt

EDAMAME AND FETA PASTA SALAD

Nutrition Facts
Per Serving
Calories 235
Total Carbs 32g
Net Carbs 25g

Ingredients

- 125g/4oz whole wheat fusilli
- 225g/8oz shelled edamame beans
- 225g/8oz cherry tomatoes
- 16 Kalamata olives, pitted and chopped
- 50g/2oz reduced-fat feta cheese, crumbled

Method

1 Cook the pasta according to the individual packet instructions.

2 Add the edamame beans to the pasta water for the final 2 minutes of cooking.

3 Drain the pasta and beans and arrange on a serving plate.

4 Mix the tomatoes, olives, garlic, and basil together in a bowl.

5 Top the pasta and beans with the tomato and olive mixture.

6 Crumble the feta cheese over the top and serve immediately.

7 Ideal served as a lunch, snack or side dish.

FROM YOUR STORE CUPBOARD
2 tsp dried basil
2 garlic cloves, crushed

GARLIC & TOMATO BUTTER BEANS

Nutrition Facts
Per Serving
Calories 147
Total Carbs 28g
Net Carbs 19g

Ingredients

- 2 400g/14oz can of diced tomatoes
- 1 400g/14oz can of butter beans, rinsed and drained
- 175g/6oz baby spinach

Method

1 Heat the oil in a large heavy-based frying pan.

2 Add the garlic and cook for 1 minute.

3 Add the remaining ingredients and cook until the spinach has wilted.

4 Season to taste and serve immediately.

5 Ideal served with whole wheat pasta and grated Parmesan cheese.

FROM YOUR STORE CUPBOARD
1 tbsp olive oil
2 garlic cloves, crushed
½ tsp Italian seasoning
Salt and pepper

ROASTED VEGETABLE MASH

Nutrition Facts
Per Serving
Calories 114
Total Carbs 17g
Net Carbs 14g

Ingredients

- 1 225g/8oz sweet potato, peeled and cut into 2-inch pieces
- 2 medium carrots, quartered
- 1 small onion, cut into thin wedges
- 1 tsp fresh ginger, grated
- 2-4 tbsp skimmed milk

Method

1 Preheat the oven to 425F/220C/Gas Mark 7.

2 Arrange the vegetables in a baking pan.

3 Add the crushed garlic and oil to the vegetables, and toss to coat well.

4 Cover the pan with foil and roast for 20 minutes.

5 Uncover the vegetables, stir and return to the oven for 15 minutes or until tender.

6 Place the vegetables in a food processor, season and add the ginger.

7 Puree the vegetables until smooth adding milk to the desired consistency.

8 Adjust the seasoning to taste and serve.

FROM YOUR STORE CUPBOARD
2 garlic cloves, crushed
4 tsp olive oil
Salt and pepper

DIABETES
Type 2
HEALING CODE

DESSERTS & SWEET TREATS

LOW CARB GREEK YOGHURT ICE CREAM

Nutrition Facts
Per Serving
Calories 127
Total Carbs 8g
Net Carbs 6g

5 Ingredients

- 60g/2½oz fat-free Greek yoghurt
- 15g/½oz vanilla protein powder
- 120ml/4floz unsweetened almond milk
- 1 tsp vanilla extract

Method

1 Put all the ingredients into a blender and pulse, until the mixture is well blended.

2 Add around 2 tablespoons of Stevia, according to your taste.

3 You can use an ice cream maker if you have one. Alternatively, place the mixture into a container and freeze. Stir the mixture every ten minutes until you have the right consistency which will take around 2 hours.

4 You can serve the ice cream straight away or keep it in the freezer for up to a week.

5 Ideal served with your favourite fresh berries and a sprinkling of chopped nuts.

FROM YOUR STORE CUPBOARD
Stevia to taste

STRAWBERRY & CHIA ICE LOLLIES

Nutrition Facts
Per Serving
Calories 63
Total Carbs 10g
Net Carbs 8g

5 Ingredients

- 165g/5½oz strawberries, sliced
- 2 tsp chia seeds
- 60ml/2floz water
- 60ml/2floz single cream

Method

1 Place the water, cream, chia seeds, and strawberries in a blender and pulse until the strawberries are completely broken up and well blended.

2 Add approximately 2 tablespoons of sweetener, according to taste.

3 Leave the mixture to thicken slightly before pouring into 4 lolly moulds.

4 Place the lollies into the freezer until completely frozen, this will take 2- 4 hours depending on your moulds and freezer.

5 Allow the lollies to rest at room temperature for 5 minutes before eating.

FROM YOUR STORE CUPBOARD
Stevia to taste

RASPBERRY & BANANA MOUSSE

Nutrition Facts
Per Serving
Calories 122
Total Carbs 19g
Net Carbs 14g

5 Ingredients

- 2 egg whites
- 60g/2½oz frozen banana
- 50g/2oz frozen raspberries

Method

1 Place the egg whites and stevia into a medium bowl.

2 Whisk with an electric whisk until the egg whites are stiff.

3 Now add the frozen fruit and blend again until evenly pink throughout.

4 Pour into a serving dish or glass and serve.

5 Decorate with a mint leaf or more berries.

FROM YOUR STORE CUPBOARD
1 tbsp Stevia

HIGH PROTEIN BERRY CRUMBLE

Nutrition Facts
Per Serving
Calories 320
Total Carbs 35g
Net Carbs 23g

5 Ingredients

- 125g/4oz raspberries or mixed berries
- 15g/½oz vanilla protein powder
- 25g/1oz uncooked oats

- 2 tbsp lemon juice
- 10 almonds, chopped

Method

1 Preheat oven to 350F/180C/Gas Mark 4.

2 Place the berries in a small ovenproof dish and sprinkle a little Stevia on top.

3 Mix the protein powder, oats, nuts, and lemon juice together to form a dry crumble.

4 Now sprinkle the crumble evenly over the berries.

5 Place on a baking tray and bake in the oven for around 15 minutes.

6 Finally, grill the crumble for a couple of minutes until the topping is golden.

7 Leave to rest for a few minutes before serving.

8 Perfect with low-carb Greek yoghurt ice cream.

FROM YOUR STORE CUPBOARD
1 tsp Stevia

PUMPKIN RASPBERRY MUFFINS

Nutrition Facts
Per Serving
Calories 83
Total Carbs 6g
Net Carbs 3g

5 Ingredients

- 175g/6oz tinned pumpkin puree
- 50g/2oz coconut flour
- 75g/3oz vanilla protein powder
- 8 egg whites
- 125g/4oz frozen raspberries

Method

1 Preheat the oven to 375F/190C/Gas Mark 5.

2 Place bun cases into a 12 holed bun tin.

3 Mix all the ingredients, except the raspberries, together in a large bowl.

4 Now, fold the raspberries carefully into the dough.

5 Spoon the mixture into the bun cases.

6 Bake the muffins for 15 minutes or until golden.

7 Leave to cool on a wire rack.

FROM YOUR STORE CUPBOARD
200g/7oz Stevia
1 tsp cinnamon
½ tsp ginger
Paper bun cases

STRAWBERRY COCONUT MINI "CHEESECAKES"

Nutrition Facts
Per Serving
Calories 132
Total Carbs 1g
Net Carbs 1g

5 Ingredients

- 400ml/14floz coconut cream
- 200g/7oz coconut oil, melted

- 1 tbsp lime juice
- 50g/2oz strawberries, chopped

Method

1 Make the coconut base by mixing half of the coconut oil with the coconut cream and approximately 1 tablespoon of Stevia.

2 Pour the coconut layer into bun tins to make 20 cheesecakes.

3 Chill in the freezer for 20 minutes.

4 Make a strawberry topping by blending the strawberries, lime juice, and the remaining coconut oil.

5 Pour over the top of the cheesecakes and chill for 2 hours or overnight.

FROM YOUR STORE CUPBOARD
Stevia to taste

SUGAR-FREE CHOCOLATE CHIP COOKIES

Nutrition Facts
Per Serving
Calories 165
Total Carbs 9g
Net Carbs 7g

5 Ingredients

- 50g/2oz butter
- 100g/3½oz Stevia
- 3 tbsp ground flax meal
- 3 tbsp water
- 75g/3oz sugar-free chocolate chips

Method

1 Preheat the oven to 325F/170/Gas Mark 3.

2 Line a baking tray with greaseproof paper.

3 Pulse the Stevia in a food processor until it is powdered.

4 Cream the butter into the Stevia until fluffy.

5 Now mix in the flax seeds, almond flour, baking powder, and water.

6 Finally, stir the chocolate chips evenly throughout the cookie dough.

7 Form the dough into 8 cookies and place onto the baking tray.

8 Bake for 15-20 minutes or until golden brown.

9 Cool on a wire rack.

10 Store the cookies for up to a week in an airtight tin.

FROM YOUR STORE CUPBOARD
150g/5oz almond flour
1 tsp baking powder

LOW CARB COOKIES 'N' ICE CREAM CAKE

Nutrition Facts
Per Serving
Calories 232
Total Carbs 34g
Net Carbs 33g

5 Ingredients

- 175g/6oz sugar-free chocolate sandwich biscuits
- 40g/1½oz reduced-fat margarine, melted
- 40g/1½oz pecans, chopped
- 1litre/1½pts diabetic vanilla ice cream

Method

1 First, crush the biscuits in a plastic bag with a rolling pin. (If you can't find sugar-free biscuits in your supermarket, you can buy them online at Amazon or other retailers).

2 Now mix the biscuit crumbs, pecans and melted margarine together.

3 Press the mixture into the base of a 15cm/6-inch square tin, reserving one third for the topping.

4 Spoon the ice cream into the tin and sprinkle over the remaining crumb mixture.

5 Freeze until firm which will take 2-3 hours.

6 Remove from the freezer and leave the cake to soften for 5 minutes.

7 Cut into 9 squares and serve.

SUGAR-FREE CHOCOLATE CAKE

Nutrition Facts
Per Serving
Calories 144
Total Carbs 21g
Net Carbs 18g

5 Ingredients

- 300ml/10½floz low-fat yoghurt
- 250ml/8½floz strong brewed coffee
- 75g/3oz cocoa powder
- 1 egg

Method

1 Preheat the oven to 350F/180C/Gas Mark 4.

2 Use cooking spray to coat a Bundt tin.

3 Mix the wet ingredients together in a small bowl until well blended.

4 Now mix the dry ingredients together in a large bowl.

5 Add the wet ingredients to the dry ingredients and mix with an electric whisk for 2-3 minutes.

6 Pour the batter into the tin.

7 Bake in the oven for around 35 minutes. Test the cake with a skewer to make sure it's cooked all the way through.

8 Leave the cake to cool on a wire rack.

9 Dust with powdered Stevia if desired.

FROM YOUR STORE CUPBOARD

200g/7oz granulated Splenda
225g/8oz self-raising flour
4 tbsp vegetable oil
2 tsp vanilla extract

DIABETIC BOUNTY BARS

Nutrition Facts
Per Serving
Calories 100
Total Carbs 7g
Net Carbs 6g

5 Ingredients

- 200g/7oz desiccated coconut
- 120ml/4floz coconut cream
- 100ml/3½floz coconut oil
- 175g/6oz sugar-free chocolate chips

Method

1 Use clingfilm to cover a 26cm/10-inch square tin.

2 Place the coconut oil in a food processor reserving 1 tablespoon for the chocolate.

3 Add the desiccated coconut, Stevia, and coconut cream.

4 Blitz until the mixture forms a dough.

5 Press the dough into the tin and freeze for 10 minutes.

6 Melt the chocolate and remaining oil in a shallow bowl in the microwave.

7 Remove the dough from the freezer and cut into 20 bars.

8 Dip the bars into the chocolate and leave to set on a rack.

9 Store in an airtight tin for up to 3 weeks.

FROM YOUR STORE CUPBOARD
50g/2oz granulated Stevia

CHOCOLATE AND AVOCADO PUDDING

Nutrition Facts
Per Serving
Calories 169
Total Carbs 13g
Net Carbs 8g

5 Ingredients

- 2 ripe avocados, halved and stoned
- 175ml/6floz coconut milk
- 40g/1½oz cocoa
- 75ml/2½floz sugar-free flavoured maple syrup

Method

1 Scoop the flesh from the avocados into a blender.

2 Now add all the remaining ingredients. You can buy diabetic maple syrup, such as 'Joseph's' online.

3 Pulse for 1 minute, scrape down the sides, then pulse again until smooth.

4 Pour the pudding into serving glasses or ramekins and chill in the fridge for at least an hour.

5 Serve decorated with sugar-free chocolate curls if desired.

FROM YOUR STORE CUPBOARD
1 tsp vanilla extract
Salt

SUGAR-FREE SHORTBREAD BISCUITS

Nutrition Facts
Per Serving
Calories 81
Total Carbs 2g
Net Carbs 1g

5 Ingredients

- 140g/4½oz almond flour
- 50g/2oz butter, softened

Method

1 Preheat the oven to 350F/180C/Gas Mark 4.

2 Cover a baking sheet with greaseproof paper.

3 Mix all the ingredients together in a food processor with a dough hook.

4 Mix the dough together until it forms a ball and chill in the fridge for 10 minutes.

5 Take a teaspoonful of dough and roll to form a small ball. Put the dough on the baking tray then flatten down with your fingers to shape the biscuit.

6 The mixture makes approximately 15 biscuits.

7 Bake the biscuits for about 8-10 minutes or until golden brown.

8 Cool on a wire rack. The biscuits will keep for up to 3 weeks in an airtight container.

FROM YOUR STORE CUPBOARD

50g/2oz granulated Stevia
½ tsp vanilla extract
Salt

DIABETIC FLOATING ISLANDS

Nutrition Facts
Per Serving
Calories 147
Total Carbs 7g
Net Carbs 7g

5 Ingredients

- 500ml/17floz milk
- 4 eggs, separated
- 2 tbsp sliced almonds
- 25g/1oz raspberries

Method

1 Place the egg yolks and 4 tablespoons of Stevia into a large bowl

2 Use an electric whisk to beat the yolks until pale.

3 Whisk in the milk and vanilla extract and transfer to a saucepan.

4 Heat the custard gently until it thickens which will take around 10 minutes. It's done when it coats the back of a spoon. Chill in the fridge for around 2 hours.

5 Make the meringue by whisking the egg whites in a large clean bowl until stiff.

6 Whisk in the remaining Stevia until the meringue is glossy and set aside.

7 Bring a large pan of boiling water to the boil and simmer gently.

8 Carefully take a ladle of meringue and drop into the water. Cook for 30 seconds on each side and place on a plate. Chill the meringues in the fridge.

9 Assemble the dessert by pouring a pool of custard into a serving dish. Top with a meringue and a sprinkling of almonds and raspberries.

FROM YOUR STORE CUPBOARD
6 tbsp granulated Stevia
1 teaspoon vanilla extract

DATE AND MUESLI SLICES

Nutrition Facts
Per Serving
Calories 91
Total Carbs 16g
Net Carbs 14g

5 Ingredients

- 2 medium apples, coarsely grated
- 5 tbsp water
- 50g/2oz margarine

- 350g/12oz dates
- 100g/3½oz no added sugar muesli

Method

1 Preheat the oven to 350F/180C/Gas Mark 4.

2 Use the cooking spray to lightly cover a 25 by 30cm/10 by 12-inch tin.

3 Put the dates, water, margarine, and apples in a saucepan and bring to the boil.

4 Cover the pan and simmer the mixture for 5 minutes or until the apple is soft.

5 Uncover the pan and cook for a further 5 minutes until the mixture resembles a paste.

6 In a frying pan toast the muesli lightly under a very low heat for 5 minutes.

7 Add the flours, cinnamon, and muesli to the date mixture and stir well.

8 Pour the batter into the tin and bake in the oven for 20 minutes until golden.

9 Cool in the tin and slice into 32 pieces.

FROM YOUR STORE CUPBOARD

Cooking spray
50g/2oz plain flour
50g/2oz wholemeal plain flour
1 tsp cinnamon

CINNAMON BAKED APPLES

SERVES 4

Nutrition Facts
Per Serving
Calories 157
Total Carbs 32g
Net Carbs 27g

5 Ingredients

- 4 large apples
- 2 tsp reduced-fat margarine
- 50g/2oz raisins
- 250ml/8½floz low-fat yoghurt

Method

1 Preheat the oven to 375F/190C/Gas Mark 5.

2 Cut a hole out of each apple removing the core.

3 Mix the Stevia, raisins, and cinnamon together until well combined.

4 Stuff the apples with the prepared raisin mixture and place in a baking dish.

5 Dot each apple with the margarine.

6 Pour the boiling water into the dish and bake for 30-45 minutes or until the apples are tender but not mushy.

7 Serve with yoghurt.

FROM YOUR STORE CUPBOARD
1 tsp cinnamon
2 tbsp granulated Stevia
175ml/6floz boiling water

HEALTHY CHOCOLATE ICE CREAM

Nutrition Facts
Per Serving
Calories 118
Total Carbs 23g
Net Carbs 17g

5 Ingredients

- 3 large frozen bananas
- 50g/2oz cocoa powder

Method

1 Place the frozen bananas in a food processor and blitz until smooth.

2 Add the vanilla extract and cocoa powder into the processor and blitz very quickly for 10 seconds.

3 Taste the ice cream and sweeten with Stevia if desired.

4 Serve immediately as soft-serve ice cream or freeze in a container for more solid ice cream if preferred.

FROM YOUR STORE CUPBOARD
Stevia to taste
1 tsp vanilla extract

RICH CUSTARD

Nutrition Facts
Per Serving
Calories 107
Total Carbs 9g
Net Carbs 9g

5 Ingredients

- 400ml/14floz semi-skimmed milk
- 4 egg yolks

Method

1 Place the milk in a heavy-based non-stick saucepan and heat until scalding but not boiling.

2 Beat the egg yolks with the Stevia in a medium bowl.

3 Blend the cornflour into the egg yolks making sure there are no lumps.

4 Pour the milk over the egg mixture whisking all the time.

5 Return the custard to the pan and cook gently on a low heat until the mixture coats the back of a spoon.

6 Serve the custard immediately with baked fruits and other desserts. You can also serve the custard chilled.

FROM YOUR STORE CUPBOARD
3 tbsp granulated Stevia
1 tbsp cornflour

FRUITY ROLL

Nutrition Facts
Per Serving
Calories 108
Total Carbs 21g
Net Carbs 19g

5 Ingredients

- 150g/5oz raisins
- 150g/5oz sultanas
- 120ml/4floz apple juice

- 125g/4oz cream cheese
- 120ml/4floz skimmed milk

Method

1 Preheat the oven to 400F/200C/Gas Mark 6.

2 Spray a baking tray with cooking spray and set aside.

3 Place the raisins, sultanas, and apple juice together in a medium bowl and cover with clingfilm.

4 Microwave on high for 5 minutes and set aside.

5 Beat the cream cheese and Stevia together in a large bowl.

6 Add the flours, milk, and cinnamon and mix to form a dough.

7 Use a rolling pin on a floured surface to roll the dough into a square approximately 35 by 25cm/14 by 10-inches.

8 Place the filling in a strip along one of the longer sides of the dough and roll up.

9 Carefully transfer the fruit roll to the baking tray and make slashes along the roll, about 1cm/½-inch apart.

10 Bake the roll for around 25 minutes until golden brown. Cut into 20 slices to serve.

FROM YOUR STORE CUPBOARD
100g/3½oz granulated Stevia
125g/4oz self-raising flour
125g/4oz wholemeal self-raising flour
Cooking spray
½ tsp cinnamon

STRAWBERRY RICOTTA CAKES

Nutrition Facts
Per Serving
Calories 98
Total Carbs 6g
Net Carbs 5g

5 Ingredients

- 500g/1lb2oz low-fat ricotta cheese
- 3 eggs, lightly beaten
- 1 tsp lemon rind
- 250g/9oz strawberries, hulled and diced

Method

1 Preheat the oven to 350F/180C/Gas Mark 4.

2 Place paper cases in an 8-hole muffin tin.

3 Beat the Stevia, ricotta, eggs and lemon rind together in a large bowl.

4 Add half of the strawberries to the mixture and stir through.

5 Pour the batter into the muffin cases and bake for 40 minutes or until golden.

6 Serve the muffins warm straight from the oven or cooled with the remaining strawberries.

FROM YOUR STORE CUPBOARD
3 tbsp granulated Stevia

WATERMELON SORBET

Nutrition Facts
Per Serving
Calories 132
Total Carbs 23g
Net Carbs 23g

5 Ingredients

- 1kilo/2¼lb seedless watermelon, cubed
- 1 400g/14oz sweetened condensed milk
- 5 tbsp lime juice

Method

1 Arrange the watermelon cubes in a single layer on a baking tray and freeze until frozen or overnight.

2 Place the watermelon, condensed milk, lime juice, and a pinch of salt into a blender and blitz until smooth.

3 Transfer the mixture into a container and freeze for around 4 hours or overnight.

4 Soften the sorbet for 5 minutes at room temperature before scooping and serving.

FROM YOUR STORE CUPBOARD
Stevia to taste
Salt

CINNAMON SWIRL PROTEIN CAKE

Nutrition Facts
Per Serving
Calories 217
Total Carbs 18g
Net Carbs 14g

5 Ingredients

- 25g/1oz uncooked oats
- 1 egg white
- 15g/½oz vanilla protein powder
- 75ml/2½floz water

Method

1 Preheat the oven to 325F/165C/Gas Mark 3.

2 Use a mini blender to blitz the oats, egg white, and water.

3 Now pour the mixture into a small bowl and whisk in 1 teaspoon of stevia and the protein powder.

4 Pour half of the batter into a small tin measuring 11 cm or 4 ½ inches across.

5 Sprinkle with 1 teaspoon of stevia and half of the cinnamon.

6 Cover with the remaining batter and sprinkle with the remaining cinnamon.

7 Bake for 25 minutes. Leave to rest for a few minutes before serving.

FROM YOUR STORE CUPBOARD
2 tsp Stevia
2 tsp cinnamon